How to use this book

Follow the advice, in italics, given for you on each page.
Support the children as they read the text that is shaded in cream.
***Praise** the children at every step!*

Detailed guidance is provided in the Read Write Inc. Phonics Handbook

8 reading activities

Children:
- *Practise reading the speed sounds.*
- *Read the green and red words for the story.*
- *Listen as you read the introduction.*
- *Discuss the vocabulary check with you.*
- *Read the story.*
- *Re-read the story and discuss the 'questions to talk about'.*
- *Re-read the story with fluency and expression.*
- *Practise reading the speed words.*

Speed sounds

Consonants *Say the pure sounds (do not add 'uh').*

f ff	l ll	m mm	n nn kn	r rr	s ss	v ve	z zz s	sh	th	(ng) nk

b bb	c k ck	d dd	g gg	h	j	p pp	qu	t (tt)	w wh	x	y	ch tch

Vowels *Say the sounds in and out of order.*

at	hen head	in	on	up	day	see happy	high	blow

zoo	look	car	for door snore	fair	whirl	shout	boy

*Each box contains one sound but sometimes more than one grapheme. Focus graphemes are **circled**.*

Green words

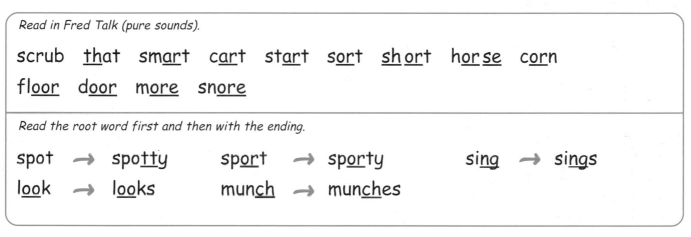

Read in Fred Talk (pure sounds).

scrub that smart cart start sort short horse corn
floor door more snore

Read the root word first and then with the ending.

spot → spotty   sport → sporty   sing → sings
look → looks   munch → munches

Red words

so of want all to do my the

Vocabulary check

Discuss the meaning (as used in the story) after the children have read each word.

definition:

munches   *chews*

scrub   *clean*

Punctuation to note in this story:

This That	*Capital letters that start sentences*
.	*Full stop at the end of each sentence*
!	*Exclamation mark used to show anger*

My sort of horse

Introduction

Did you know there were many sorts of horses?
Did you know that a horse can play the piano?

My sort of horse

Story written by Gill Munton
Illustrated by Tim Archbold

This sort of horse

is a sporty horse.

That sort of horse

pulls a cart.

This sort of horse

has spotty shorts.

That sort of horse

looks so smart.

This sort of horse

munches on corn.

That sort of horse

sings all day.

This sort of horse

can scrub the floor.

That sort of horse

wants to play.

This sort of horse

can unlock the door.

That sort of horse

starts to snore.

But this sort of horse – is *my* sort of horse!

And I do not need 1 thing more!

Questions to talk about

Re-read the page. Read the question to the children.

FIND IT

✓ *Turn to the page*

✓ *Read the question*

✓ *Find the answer*

FIND IT	*2 horses that like dressing up*
FIND IT	*2 hard working horses*
FIND IT	*a hungry horse*
FIND IT	*2 horses that like music*
FIND IT	*a horse that makes a noise*

Which sort of horse would you like to live with you?